YOU ARE HERE

A Guide to Everyday Maps, Plans, and Diagrams

by Stephen Martin

The Peoples Publishing Group, Inc.

Free to Learn, to Grow, to Change

ISBN 0-88336-499-9

© 1990

The Peoples Publishing Group, Inc.
230 West Passaic Street
Maywood, New Jersey 07607

Printed in the United States of America.

Supervising Editor: Kathleen Wright
Illustrations and cover design by Patricia Rapple
Design by Mary H. Greenseich

9 8 7 6 5 4 3

Table of Contents

To the Teacher — Using You Are Here:

You Are Here is written to help students visualize what is represented in maps, plans, and diagrams. It is intended to help students who look at maps and see only a meaningless maze of lines. The tone is intentionally light-hearted, but adult.

For some people, maps are totally undecipherable. To make map-decoding easier, **You Are Here** begins with a core of the small and the familiar. Starting with simple floor plans allows the student to extend the abstraction outward from his immediate environment, to progressively larger areas: buildings, neighborhoods, cities, and regions.

Since the complexity of the material increases gradually, the pace of introducing the chapters will depend on the students. Students should be given as much extra practice as time allows for the lessons on grids, scale, and compass directions.

A key concept in the book is the map as an aerial or top view of the world. You can help reinforce and clarify this concept when introducing each chapter. Aerial photographs, when available, are helpful to show how flat and small things look when viewed from above.

Freely introduce maps from your own community in the appropriate chapters. The maps in the book are simpler than standard maps. Therefore, be sure students have all the concepts needed before exposing them to more complicated maps.

The book can be used by the student alone or in one-on-one instruction. You can also experiment with using the book with small groups of 3 - 4 students. Act as facilitator, but allow the students to work on the exercises in a group. Students can help one another, check each others' answers, and share explanations. You should monitor the groups, offer suggestions and information, and reinforce helpful behavior.

New Readers Press would like to learn about your successes and any problems you and students may experience while using **You Are Here**.

To the Student:

The goal of this book is to teach you about maps. Maps make it easier to get around. **You Are Here** uses ordinary maps that you see every day.

The answers to the exercises are found in the back of the book on pages **78, 79,** and **80.** To get the most from this book, do not look at the answers until you have finished the exercises.

Please feel free to write to us. Our address is on the back of the book. Tell us how you feel about **You Are Here**.

INTRODUCTION

Finding places in your own neighborhood is easy. Everything is familiar to you. But what if you were in a strange place? You wouldn't know your way around. You would need something to help you.

You would need a <u>map</u>.

Maps help us to find places. Maps are pictures that make it easy to see where things are. They show us the way.

Chapter 1: FLOOR PLANS

WORDS TO KNOW

map	floor plan	top view

There are many different types of maps. A map of a room or a building is called a <u>floor plan</u>. The floor plan of a room shows where all the windows and doors are. It shows where the furniture is placed.

Most maps look like they were drawn looking down from high above.

This is a picture of the Franklin Office Building. Dr. Brown has an office here. There are other offices in this building.

Like most maps, floor plans are drawn from a top view. First, you must find the shape of the room. Begin with a top view. Imagine yourself high above an empty room looking down. What you see below you is the floor. Dr. Brown's office floor is shaped like a rectangle. Each side of the rectangle is one wall. Below is an outline of Dr. Brown's office.

Now the windows and doors must be drawn. On floor plans,

windows are drawn like .   Doors are drawn like   .

Dr. Brown's office has one door and three windows.

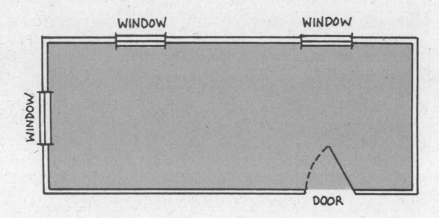

Finally, the furniture must be drawn. Furniture is shown by simple shapes. In Dr. Brown's office there is a small, round table, a bookcase, and a desk and chair. Like the floor plan, all the furniture is shown from a top view.

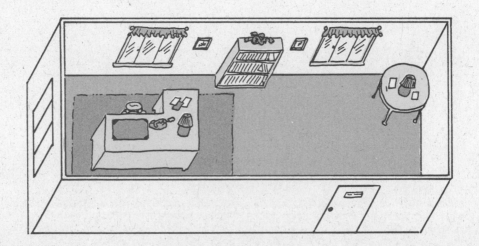

When looking down from above, what you see below you is the top of the furniture. The round table in Dr. Brown's office is shown by the symbol ⬭. The bookcase is shown by the symbol ▭. The desk and chair are shown by the symbol ▭. The floor plan with the furniture included looks like:

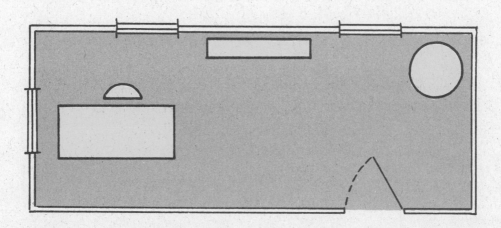

Label each item in the floor plan of Dr. Brown's office. Include the windows and doors:

    a.   Put a "**T**" on the small, round table.
    b.   Put a "**DC**" on the desk and chair.
    c.   Put a "**B**" on the bookcase.
    d.   Put a "**W**" on the windows.
    e.   Put a "**D**" on the door.

Dr. Green has an office next to Dr. Brown's office. Use the floor plan of Dr. Green's office to answer the following questions:

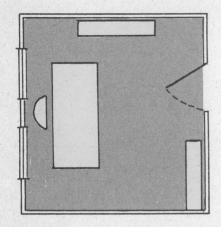

1. How many windows are in Dr. Green's office? _____

2. How many doors are in Dr. Green's office? _____

3. How many bookcases are in Dr. Green's office? _____

The Franklin Office Building has many offices. One of the offices belongs to Dr. Gray. Draw a floor plan of Dr. Gray's office.

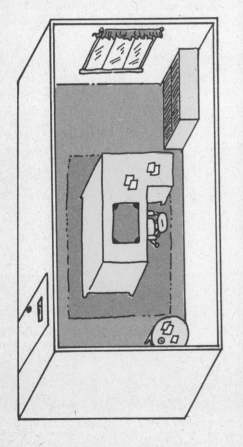

Draw a floor plan of the room you are in right now. Design your own symbols if needed. Include only the large pieces of furniture.

Draw a floor plan of your own living room. Design your own symbols if needed. Include only the large pieces of furniture.

Draw a floor plan for each room shown in the following pictures. Design your own symbols if needed.

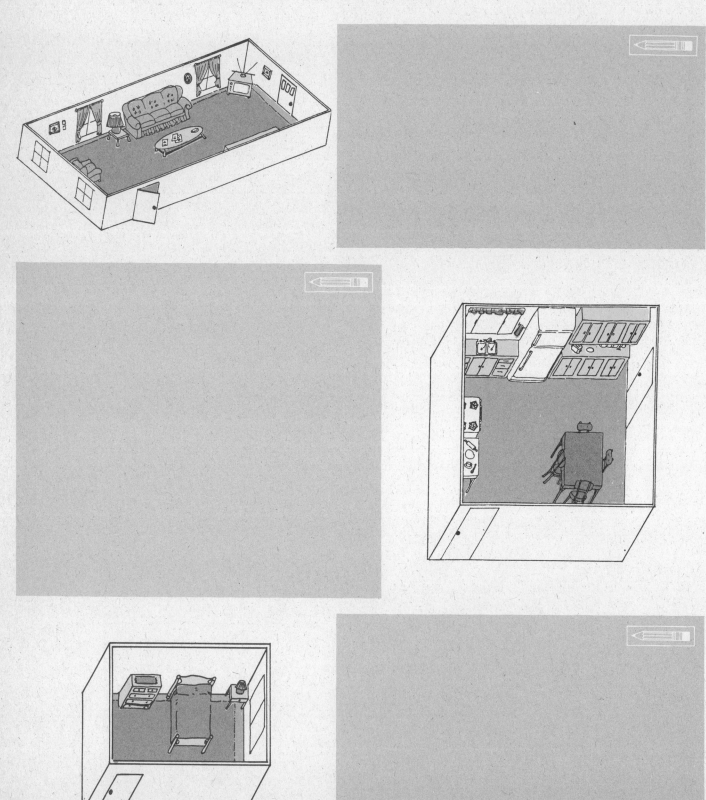

Chapter 2: FLOOR PLANS OF BUILDINGS

Floor plans can show more than one room. Some floor plans show several rooms. There are floor plans of whole buildings.

In the last chapter, you saw the floor plans of Dr. Brown's and Dr. Green's offices. You drew a floor plan for Dr. Gray's office. All these offices are in the same building. They share the same waiting room.

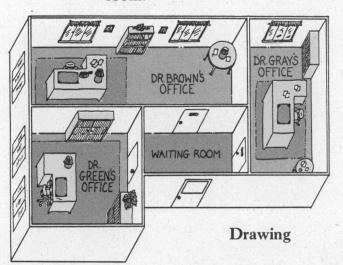

Drawing

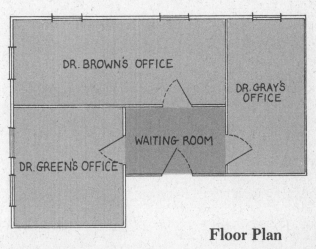

Floor Plan

1. What is shown in the drawing, but not in the floor plan?

   _____

2. Floor plans of buildings do not show furniture. They only show rooms.

   a. How many doors do you see in the floor plan? _____

   b. How many windows do you see in the floor plan? _____

   c. Draw the symbol for a door. _____

   d. Draw the symbol for a window. _____

The three doctors' offices are on one floor of the Franklin Office Building. There are many other offices on the same floor. Look at the floor plan below. Find the three doctors' offices. Find their waiting room.

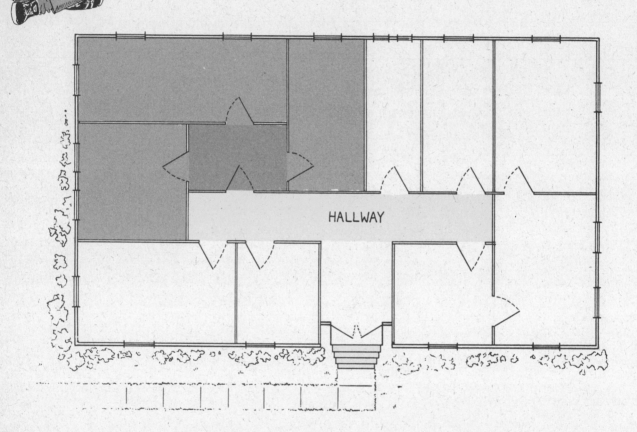

STAIRS

HALLWAY

1. How many rooms are shown in the floor plan?

_____

2. Find the hallway. How many doors lead directly into the

hallway? _____

3. Find the front doors. Just outside the front doors you will see

. What does this symbol stand for? _____

Draw a floor plan for the office building below. Design your own symbols if needed.

Think about the room you are in now. What is on the other side of each wall? Your answers might be — another room, a hall, or the outside.

1. _____

2. _____

3. _____

4. _____

What is above the ceiling? What is below the floor?

1. _____

2. _____

Draw a floor plan of the main floor of your own home. Design your own symbols if needed.

YOUR TURN

Sun Company makes sunglasses. They need to build a new office building. They have asked you to draw the floor plans. In this building they need:

— 3 small offices
— 2 larger offices
— 1 large meeting room

Draw a set of floor plans that will meet Sun Company's needs. The people in the offices want a lot of outside light. Be sure to include many windows. Design your own symbols if needed.

Chapter 3: STREET MAPS

WORDS TO KNOW

street map   intersection

Floor plans help us to find our way inside buildings and houses. Street maps help us to get from place to place in neighborhoods or cities.

The Franklin Office Building is on Oak Drive. Across the street is a small store. A park is nearby.

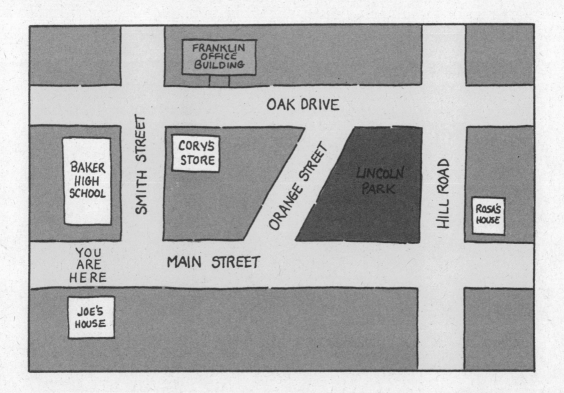

Above is a street map of the neighborhood around the Franklin Office Building. Dr. Brown has an office in this building. Look closely at the map. Find the Franklin Office Building. It is colored blue on the map. Finish the sentences below.

1. The name of the store across the street from the Franklin

   Office Building is _____.

2. _____ High School is on Smith Street.

3. The name of the park is _____.

Joe's house is on Main Street. Find Main Street on the map above. Now find Joe's house.

Joe did not know how to get from his house to Dr. Brown's office. Joe called Dr. Brown on the telephone. "I live in the big, white house on Main Street," he said. "How do I get to your office?"

Dr. Brown gave him these directions: "As you leave your house turn right on Main Street. When you reach Smith Street turn left. Go down Smith Street until you reach Oak Drive. Turn right on Oak Drive. You will see the Franklin Office Building on the left-hand side of Oak Drive. My office is on the first floor."

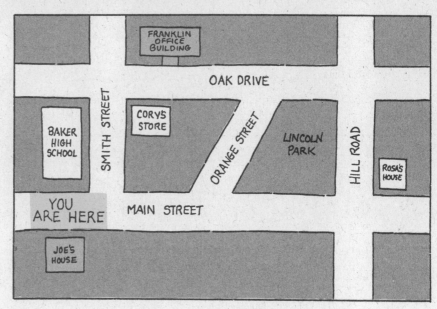

Find Joe's house again on the map above. Put your finger on the spot marked "You Are Here." With your finger, follow the directions Dr. Brown gave to Joe. Did you get to Dr. Brown's office?

Use the map above to answer the following questions.

1. Which is longer, Oak Drive or Hill Road? _____

    _____

2. Rosa's house is across the street from _____

    _____.

3. Which is closer to Cory's store, Joe's house or Rosa's house?

    _____

4. Is Lincoln Park closer to Orange Street or Smith Street?

    _____

INTERSECTIONS

An intersection is a place where things cross. On a map, an intersection is where streets cross each other.

Look at the map below. Two streets are colored yellow. One is Washington Street. The other is Fifth Avenue. Find them. Put your finger on the place where they cross. We call this place the intersection of Washington Street and Fifth Avenue.

Find the library on the map. It is colored blue. It is at the intersection of Washington Street and Fifth Avenue. Two streets go by the library. Washington Street goes past the front of the library. Fifth Avenue goes past one side of the library. The library is on the corner of Washington Street and Fifth Avenue. We call this corner the intersection of Washington Street and Fifth Avenue.

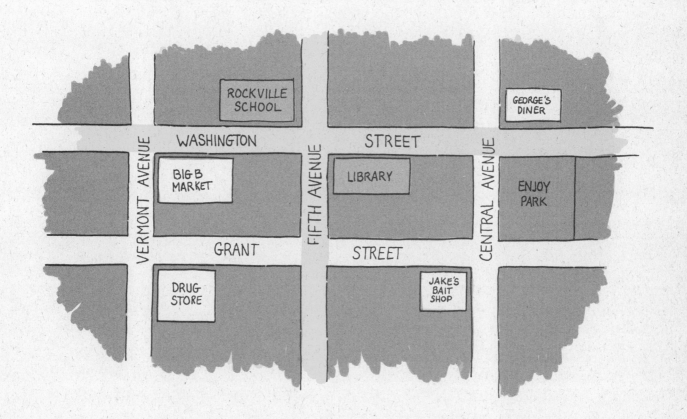

1. There are four corners at the intersection of Washington Street and Fifth Avenue. What other building is at the intersection of Washington Street and Fifth Avenue?

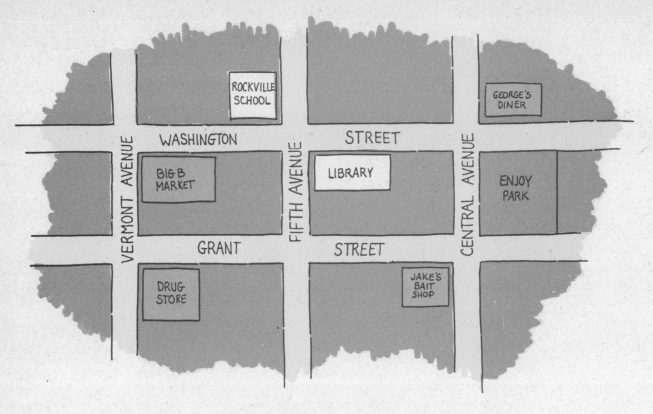

Look at the map above. Fill in the blanks.

1. _____ and _____
   are at the intersection of Grant Street and Central Avenue.

2. The _____ is at
   the intersection of Washington Street and Vermont Avenue.

3. The drug store is at the intersection of _____

   and _____ .

4. George's Diner is at the intersection of _____

   and _____ .

Chapter 4: MAP SYMBOLS

WORDS TO KNOW

symbol	key	road map	route	expressway

A <u>symbol</u> is a picture that stands for a thing or idea. Symbols often replace words on a map. In the floor plan, we used symbols to show furniture. A table looked like ⬤ . A bookcase looked like ▬ . Maps often use symbols to show houses, bridges, and trees. Most symbols look like the things they stand for. Symbols make maps easier to use. They take up little space. Yet, they give needed information.

 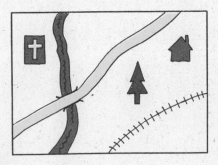

This map uses the symbol to stand for a church. The symbol ⟝⟞ stands for a bridge. Compare the picture to the map. Can you tell what these symbols stand for?

1. 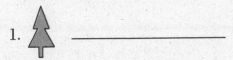 _____   2.  _____

3. ┼┼┼┼ _____   4. ∿∿∿ _____

SYMBOLS ARE FOUND IN THE MAP KEY

Most maps have a <u>key</u>. The map key tells about the map. The map key explains all symbols used on the map.

Look at the map below. Find the map key. Use the map key to answer the following questions.

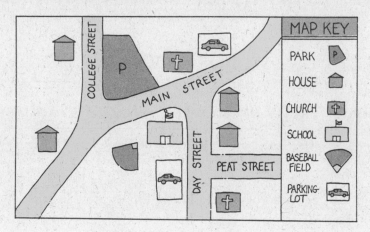

1. The symbol ⬡ stands for a _____.

2. The symbol ⬠ stands for a _____.

3. The symbol for a school looks like _____.

4. The symbol for a park looks like _____.

5. How many churches are shown on the map? _____

6. The park is at the intersection of _____

   and _____.

SYMBOLS ON ROAD MAPS

A road map is not the same as a street map. A road map shows expressways. It tells us where cities and towns are and how to get to them. Road maps show large areas.

Remember that maps show what you see from high above. Road maps only show the important things. They do not show buildings. Road maps show roads and towns or cities.

Road maps use many symbols. Travelers use these symbols to help them plan their trips. Symbols on a road map show the best roads to take. The symbol for a road is one line. Three lines show expressways. Dots show small towns. Shapes show large cities.

Below is a map of Baker County. Use it to do the following:

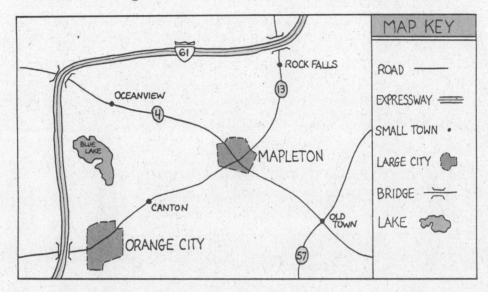

1. Draw the symbol for a small town. _____

2. Draw the symbol for a large city. _____

3. Name all the small towns on the map. _____

_____

4. Name all the large cities on the map. _____

_____

Look at the road between Oceanview and Old Town. The road has a number on it. Most roads that go between towns have numbers. Roads with numbers are also called <u>routes</u>. These numbers help travelers to stay on the right roads.

5. The number on the road between Oceanview and Old Town

is _____.

All the roads on this map are numbered. One of the roads is an expressway. Traffic travels fast on expressways. Expressways usually do not have stoplights.

1. Look again at the map key of Baker County. What is the

    number of the expressway on the map?_____

2. What two routes could be used to go from Rock Falls to

    Orange City? _____ and _____

Mrs. Lee lives in Rock Falls. She wants to go to Orange City. She is trying to decide if she should take Route 13 or Route 61.
    Help Mrs. Lee decide which route to take. Look at the map below.

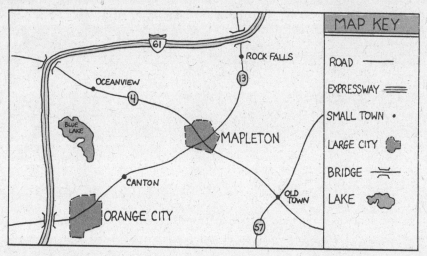

3. Which route would you take? Why? _____

    _____

    _____

There are two routes Mrs. Lee could have taken. Mrs. Lee took Route 13. If she were in a hurry, she would have taken Route 61. Route 61 is the expressway. Even though the expressway is a little longer, it would be faster.

Mrs. Lee was not in a hurry. That is why she drove on Route 13. Also, she needed to stop at a store to buy a new rake. Mapleton has a hardware store. She bought a new rake there.

MORE SYMBOLS

Symbols can show almost anything on a map. Below is a map of the United States. This map shows where natural resources are found. The mapmaker uses the symbol ⛽ to show where oil is found. The symbol looks like an oil well.

In Texas, the symbol for an oil well looks like .

In California, the symbol for an oil well looks like ⛽ .

1. Which state makes more oil, Texas or California?

_____

If you said Texas, you were correct. A large symbol means that there is a lot of the product. A small symbol means the product can be found there, but there is not very much.

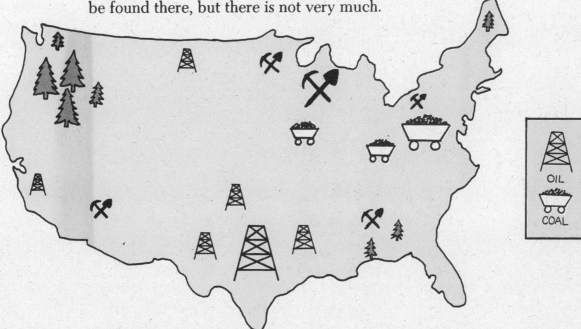

Use the map to do the following:

1. Draw a ⭕ around the biggest oil-making area in the United States.

2. Draw a △ around the biggest coal-making area.

3. Draw a ▭ around the biggest iron ore-making area.

4. Draw a ◇ around the biggest lumber-making area.

MAKE YOUR OWN MAP

Yourtown is a small village that you are about to create. In the village there are:

— 3 houses
— 1 park
— 1 town hall
— 1 library
— 2 stores

On the map key, draw a symbol for each of the places listed. Then using your symbols, draw a map of Yourtown.

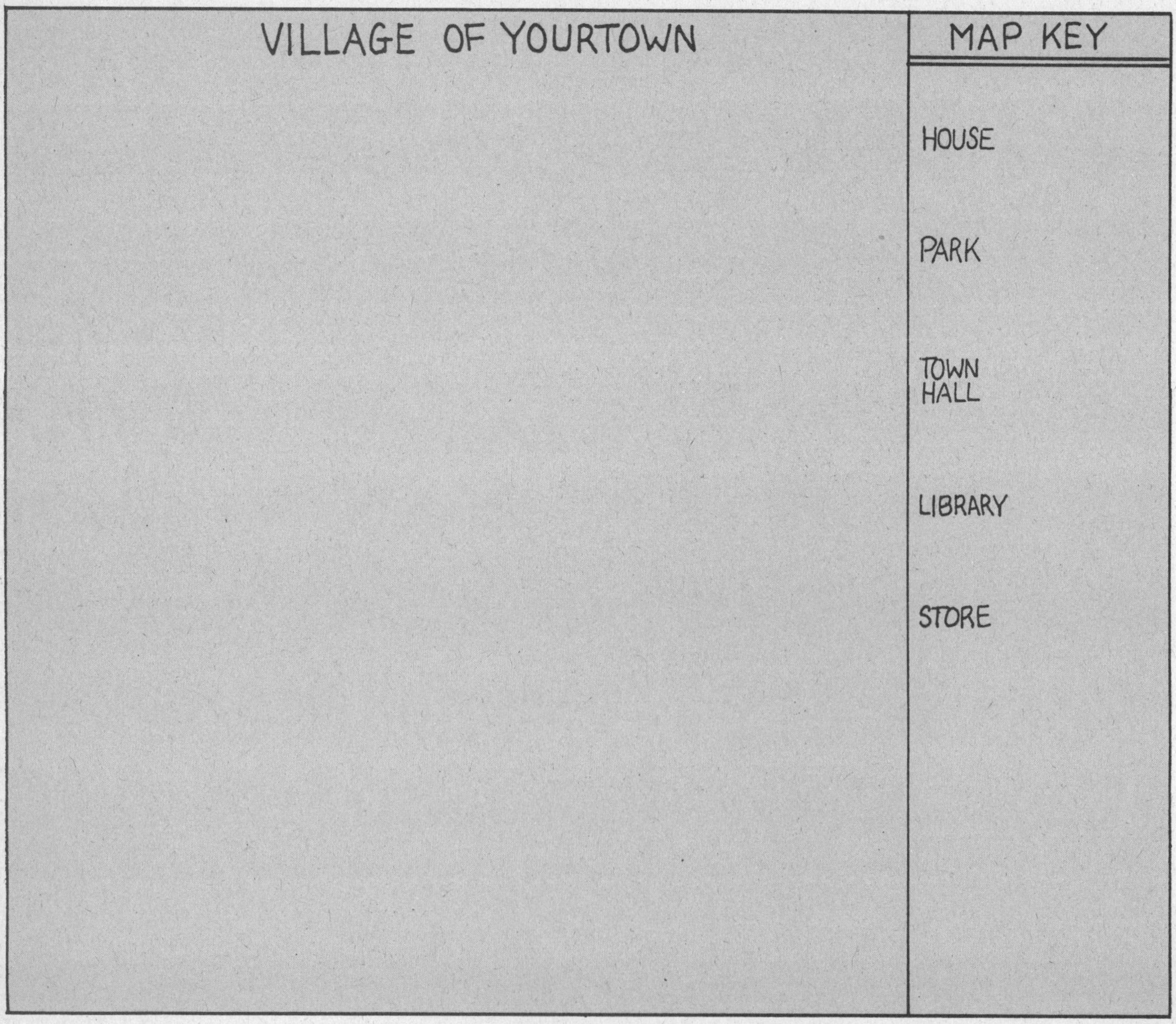

VILLAGE OF YOURTOWN

MAP KEY

HOUSE

PARK

TOWN HALL

LIBRARY

STORE

Chapter 5: STREET MAPS AND GRIDS

WORDS TO KNOW

grid   index

The Franklin Office Building is in the village of Springfield. The building is shown on the map.

Look closely at the map. Can you find the library?

How long did it take you?

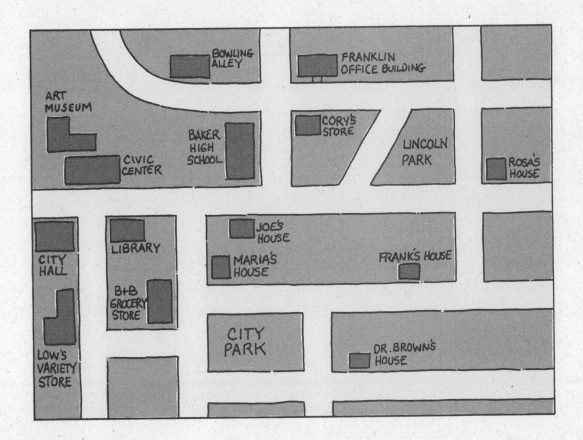

It is sometimes hard to find places on large maps. Large maps show many roads. They show many buildings.

There is something on this map that will help you. It is called a <u>grid</u>.

A grid is a crisscross of lines. Some lines run up and down. Some lines run across.

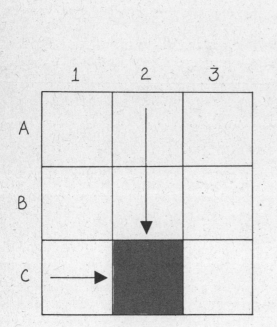

The lines form squares. Count the number of squares. Did you count nine squares?

Look at the shaded square. It is square 2C. Each square is named by a number and a letter. The number comes first and then the letter.

Using the grid, find square 2C. Use one finger from each hand. Follow these steps.

1. Find the number "2." Put your finger on it.
2. Move your finger from the number "2" **down** the row of squares. Stop when you reach the shaded square.
3. Find the letter "C." Put another finger on it.
4. Move your finger from the letter "C" **across** the row of squares. Stop when you reach the shaded square. Where your two fingers meet is square 2C.

Using the grid, you have found square 2C.

The map below has a grid. Use it to answer the following questions.

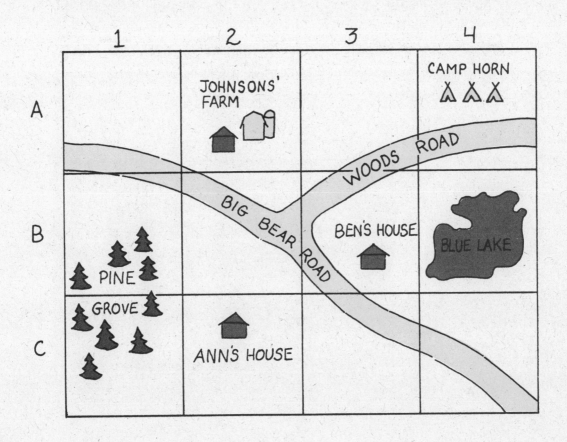

1. Johnsons' farm is in square _____.

2. Blue Lake is in square _____.

3. Ann's house is in square _____.

4. Whose house is in square 3B? _____

5. What is in both squares 1B and 1C? _____

Maps with grids often have an index. An <u>index</u> lists all the important places on the map. Next to each place is the number and the letter of a grid square. You can use the grid square to find the place on the map.

Below is part of an index for the **map of Springfield**. Use it to find each of the places listed. Put an "X" on each one as you find it.

Place	Grid Box
B & B Grocery	1C
City Hall	1B
Civic Center	1B
Cory's Store	3A
Low's Variety Store	1C
Art Museum	1A
Rosa's house	4B

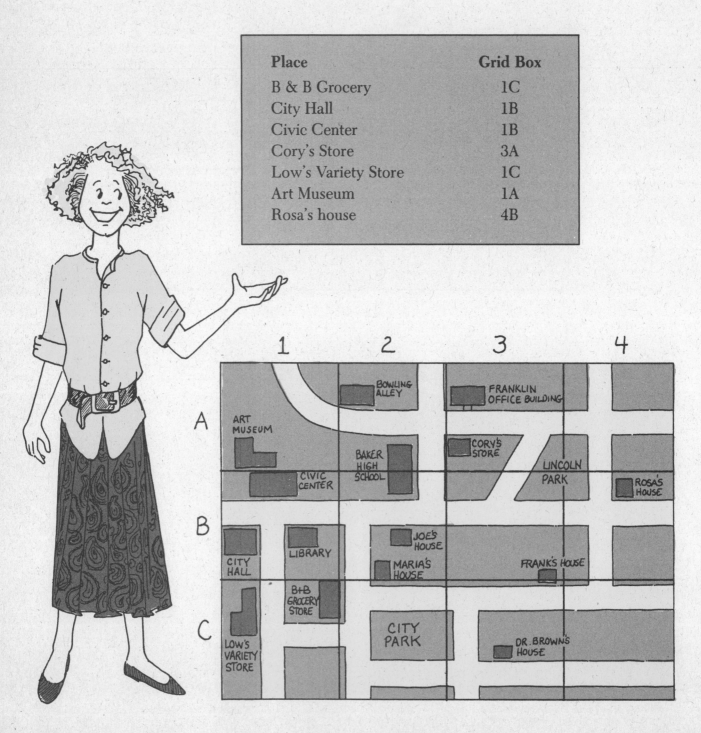

Grids are often used to find streets. Use the grid, and find all the streets in the index. Color in the whole length of each street as you find it. The first one is done for you.

Street	Grid Box
Finch Path	3D
Bay Drive	4B
Ocean Drive	1B
Kingman Road	3B
Rose Street	5E
Rivercrest Road	5D
Woodside Lane	1D

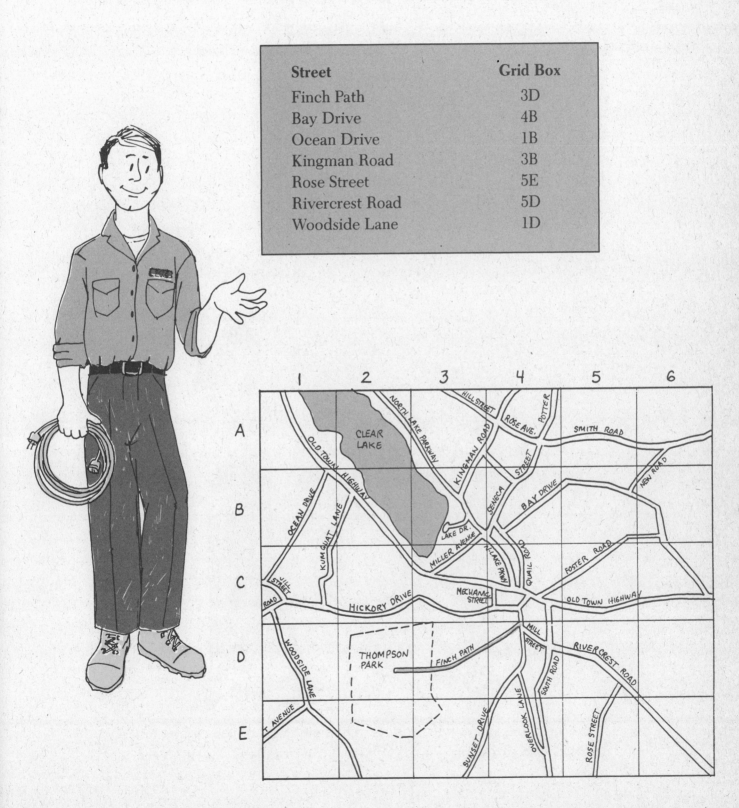

Chapter 6: DIRECTIONS ON A MAP

WORDS TO KNOW

compass

A globe is a map of the world. It is round like the earth. But most maps are drawn on sheets of paper. They do not take up as much room as globes. They are easy to carry. Paper maps can be folded and put away.

Paper maps have one problem. On a paper map, you cannot tell which side is the top. On a globe, the North Pole is always at the top.

Try this experiment. Take a plain piece of paper. Draw a square in the center. Fold the paper up neatly. Pick up the paper and turn it around several times. Now unfold the paper. You probably cannot tell where the top of your square is. Now draw an arrow pointing to the top of your square. Fold your paper and turn it again. You will always know which way is up.

On a globe, north is always up ↑ . South is always down ↓ .

East is always to the right ➤ . West is always to the left ◄ .

Since the top of the globe is north, the top of the map is almost always north also. Mapmakers usually let you know which edge of the map is the top.

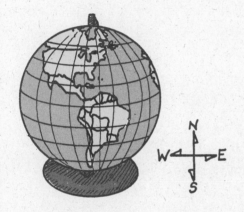

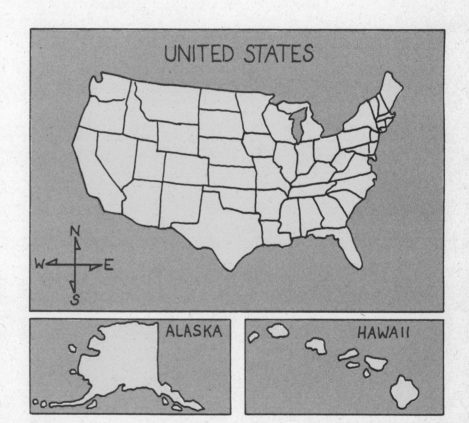

MAPS HAVE A COMPASS

Mapmakers put <u>compasses</u> on their maps to help people to find direction. A compass shows that north is up ↑ . South is down ↓ .

East is to the right ➤ . West is to the left ◄ .

SOME MAPS DON'T HAVE A COMPASS

Some maps do not have compasses. Can you find direction on this type of map?

"Which way is up?"

The maps below do not have compasses. They are made so that north is at the top of the map. Maps without compasses are usually made this way — north is at the top.

Draw compasses on each of the three maps below.

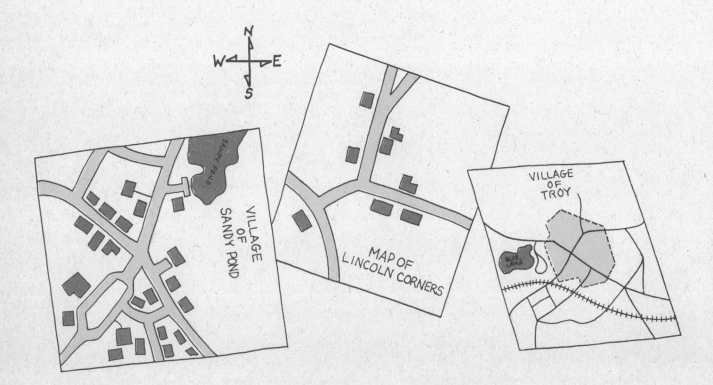

Joe is trying to make a map of Turkey Creek. But Joe has a problem. He doesn't know which way north is. Look closely at the map. Do you see anything on the map that would help Joe?

Can you help Joe? Draw a compass on the map below.

Rosa is looking for Joe's house. She does not have a map. Rosa knows if she starts in the right direction she will find the way. She knows Joe lives on the south side of town. Help Rosa find the right direction.

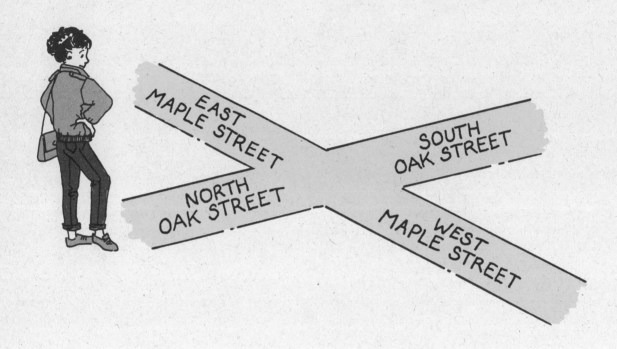

Choose the best answer.

1. Joe lives on the south side of town. To get to Joe's house Rosa

   should _____.
   a. turn left at the intersection
   b. go straight through the intersection
   c. turn right at the intersection

Chapter 7: SCALE

WORDS TO KNOW

scale	line scale

Have you ever seen a model car? Model cars look very much like real cars. Of course, model cars are much smaller.

Model cars are built to <u>scale</u>. That means **everything is made smaller by the same amount**.

1. Which model car is built to scale, "A" or "B"? _____

Model A is built to scale. Everything in model A is made smaller by the same amount. Model B is not built to scale. The tires are too large. They were not made smaller by the same amount as the rest of the car.

Maps are models of real places. Maps are drawn to scale. Everything on a map is made smaller by the same amount.

Alaska is our largest state. It is larger than Texas. If a map of the United States were not drawn to scale, Alaska might look like a small state. That would not be true. In order for maps to be accurate, everything on the map has to be made smaller by the same amount.

Map Not Drawn To Scale

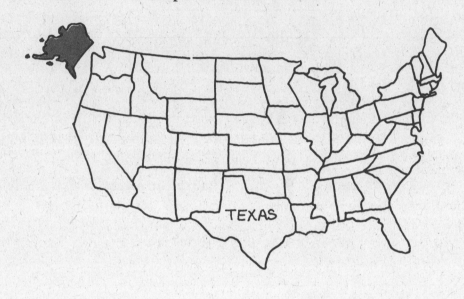

TEXAS

Map Drawn To Scale

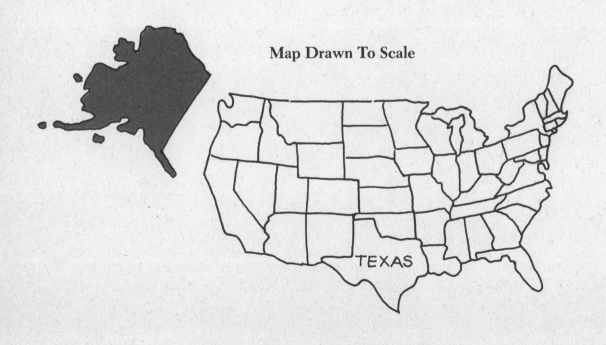

TEXAS

THE SCALE ON A MAP

The scale on a map compares the map distance to the true distance. By using the scale on a map, you can tell how far away places are. On a map, things might look like they are close together. But they really may be miles apart. A scale will tell you how far away things really are.

For example, let's say it is 10 miles from your house to your friend's house. The map shows that the two houses are only one inch apart. For this map, the scale is 1 inch = 10 miles.

Each map has its own scale. On this map 1 inch = 100 miles. How many miles are shown by:

1. Two inches? _____

2. Three inches? _____

3. Five inches? _____

4. One-half inch? _____

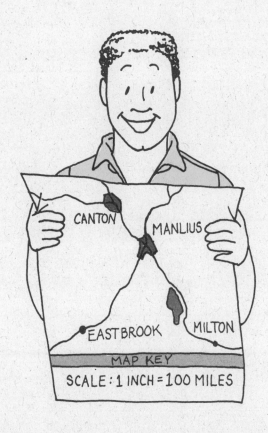

FINDING THE SCALE

To find the scale on a map, look at the map key.
Find the scales on these maps.

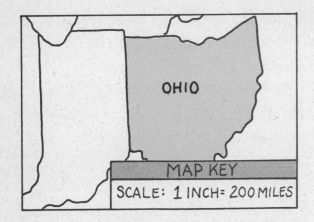

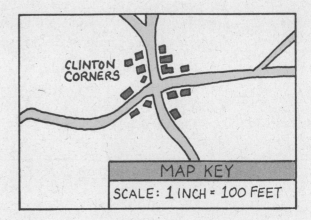

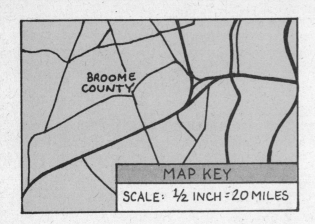

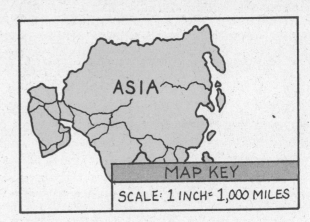

The scale on the map of Ohio is 1 inch = 200 miles.

1. What is the scale on the map of Clinton Corners?

    _____

2. What is the scale on the map of Broome County?

    _____

3. What is the scale on the map of Asia?

    _____

To do this exercise, you will need a ruler.

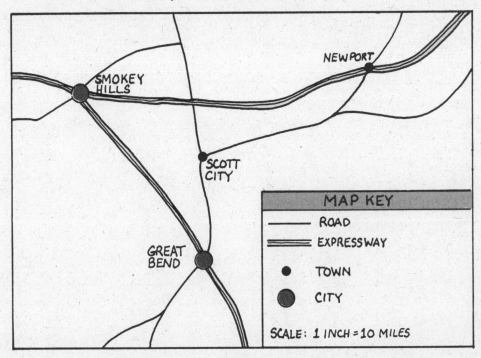

1. a. Look at the map key. What is the scale on this map?

   _____

   b. Use your ruler and measure the distance between Smokey Hills and Great Bend. The distance between Smokey Hills and Great Bend is _____ inches.

   c. Use the scale of 1 inch = 10 miles. The actual distance between Smokey Hills and Great Bend is _____.

   d. About how many miles is it between Scott City and Newport? _____

   e. About how many miles is it between Great Bend and Scott City? _____

   f. About how many miles is it between Smokey Hills and Newport? _____

USING A LINE SCALE

Some maps have a different way to show the scale. Look at the map below. Find the map key.

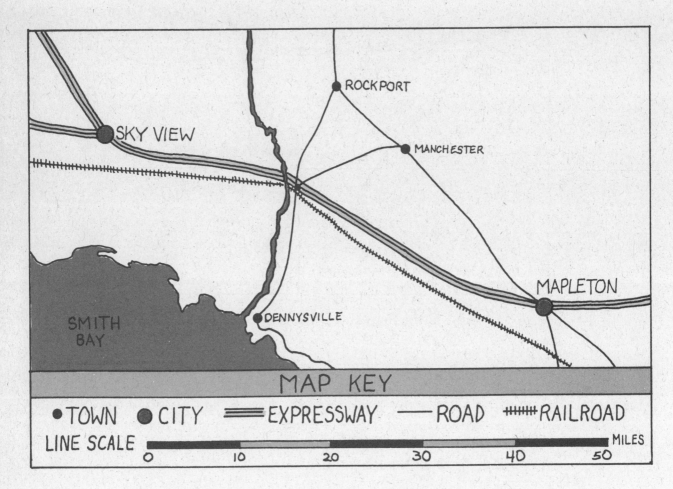

The key shows a <u>line scale</u>. It looks like ▬▬▬▬▬. To use the line scale, measure the distance between two places on the map. Measure the same distance on the line scale. The line scale tells you how far apart the two places are. It tells you the true distance.

Use the line scale and map on page 46 for this exercise. The pictures will help to guide you.

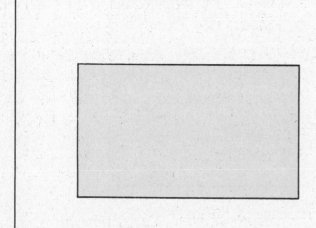

1. Get a blank sheet of paper.

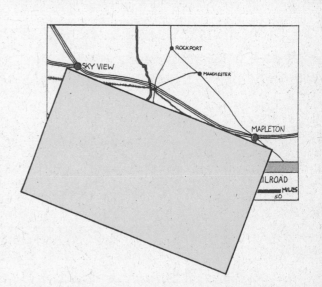

2. Put your paper on the map so that the edge of the paper connects Sky View and Mapleton.

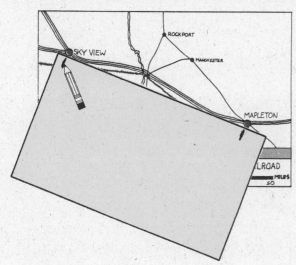

3. Make two small marks on your paper where Sky View and Mapleton are.

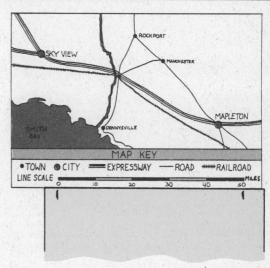

4. Put your paper next to the line scale. Place the first mark you made next to the zero. Where does the second mark fall on the scale? Read the scale at the second mark. Read the number on the scale.

According to the scale, the distance between Sky View and Mapleton is 50 miles.

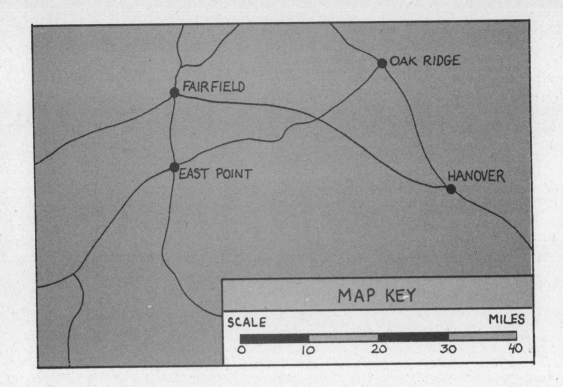

Look at the map above. Find the line scale. Use the line scale to help you answer the following questions.

1. About how many miles is it between Oak Ridge and

   Fairfield? _____

2. About how many miles is it between East Point and

   Hanover? _____

3. About how many miles is it between Oak Ridge and

   Hanover? _____

4. About how many miles is it between East Point and

   Fairfield? _____

Chapter 8: MALL MAPS

WORDS TO KNOW

directory

Shopping malls are good places to shop. All the stores are in one large building. But if you have never been to a mall before, it can be confusing. It can be hard to find the store you want.

To help you, most malls have maps. These maps show all the stores in the mall. Usually there is a map at each entrance.

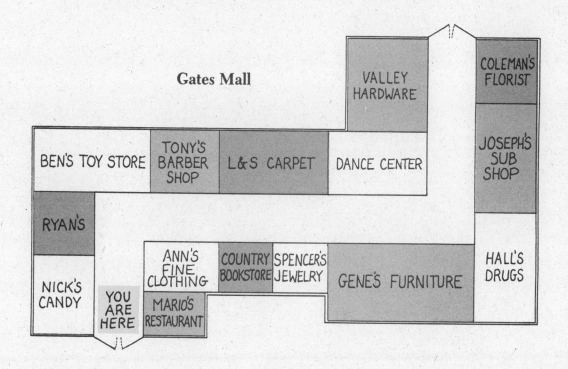

Gates Mall

Gates Mall

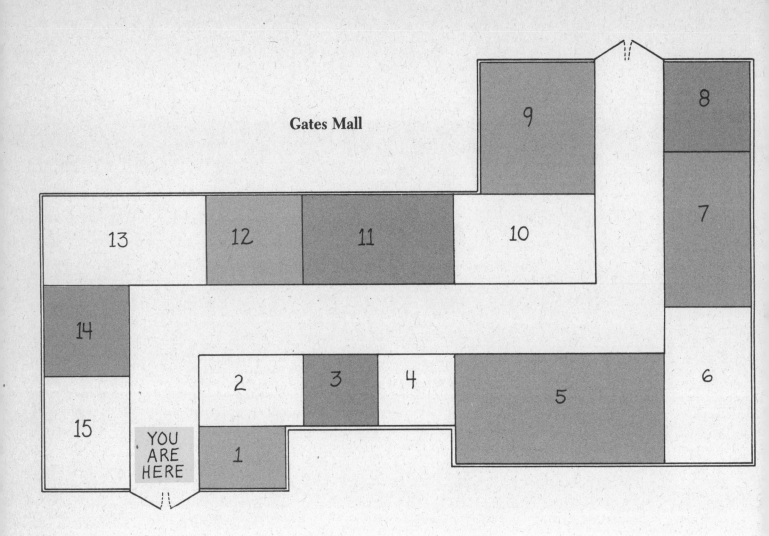

Gates Mall Directory			
Ann's Fine Clothing	2	L & S Carpet	11
Ben's Toy Store	13	Mario's Restaurant	1
Coleman's Florist	8	Nick's Candy	15
Country Bookstore	3	Ryan's	14
Dance Center	10	Spencer's Jewelry	4
Gene's Furniture	5	Tony's Barber Shop	12
Hall's Drugs	6	Valley Hardware	9
Joseph's Sub Shop	7		

Look closely at the map. Each store has a number. Find store number 1 on the map. Find store number 2. Choose the best answer.

1. Store number 2 is _____ .
   a. next to store number 1
   b. across from store number 1
   c. down the mall from store number 1

Look at all the store numbers. The numbers and store names are listed in the map <u>directory</u>. The directory is like an index. The list is in alphabetical order. Follow the numbers around the mall.

2. Use the map and the directory to complete the following exercise.

   a. Gene's Furniture is store number _____ .
      Find Gene's Furniture on the map. Put a "G" on it.

   b. Ben's Toy Store is store number _____ .
      Find Ben's Toy Store. Put a "B" on it.

   c. L & S Carpet is store number _____ . Find
      L & S Carpet on the map. Put an "L" on it.

   d. Ann's Fine Clothing is store number _____ .
      Find Ann's Fine Clothing on the map. Put an "A" on it.

Joe and Rosa went into Gates Mall. They found the mall map at the entrance.

Joe said, "I'm looking for Spencer's Jewelry."

Rosa looked at the directory. "It's store number 4," she said.

Joe found store number 4 on the map. "It's easy to find," he said. "We just go straight ahead until we come to the end. Then we turn right. Spencer's Jewelry is the third store on the right."

Look at the map of Gates Mall. Put your pencil on the spot marked, "You Are Here." Trace the path that Joe and Rosa took to Spencer's Jewelry.

Chapter 9: WEATHER MAPS

WORDS TO KNOW

forecast	rain	showers

Are you planning a picnic tomorrow? You had better check the weather map. Picnics in the rain are not fun.

A <u>forecast</u> tells us what kind of weather is coming. Weather maps forecast the weather.

Choose the best answer.

1. A forecast tells us _____.
   a. yesterday's weather
   b. the weather right now
   c. what kind of weather is coming

To read a weather map you must understand the symbols. Like other maps, symbols are explained in the map key.

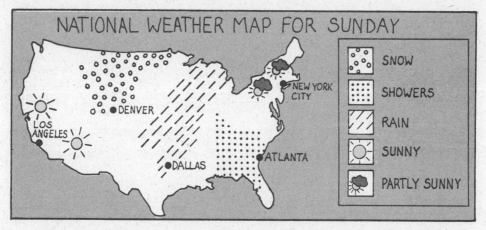

Above is a weather map of the United States. Use it to help you answer the following questions.

1. Look at the top of the map. Choose the best answer.

   This map forecasts _____.
   a. Friday's weather
   b. Sunday's weather
   c. Tuesday's weather

2. is the symbol for _____.

3. is the symbol for _____.

4. is the symbol for _____.

5. The symbol for sunny looks like _____.

6. The symbol for rain looks like _____.

7. According to the weather map, the forecast for Dallas is

   _____.

8. The forecast for Denver is _____.

9. The forecast for Los Angeles is _____.

10. The forecast for New York City is _____.

11. The forecast for Atlanta is _____.

RAIN OR SHOWERS

The terms "rain" and "showers" are often confusing. ///// is

the symbol for rain. This means it will probably rain steadily.

:::: is the symbol for showers. This means it will probably rain

on and off for short periods of time.

Choose the best answers.

1. ///// on a weather map means it will probably _____.

    a. rain steadily
    b. rain on and off
    c. snow

2. :::: on a weather map means it will probably _____.

    a. rain steadily
    b. rain on and off
    c. snow

Like many places, parks have maps, too. There is usually a large map at the entrance gate. Many parks give out maps at the entrance and at the ranger station. Below is a map of Morgan State Park.

Morgan State Park

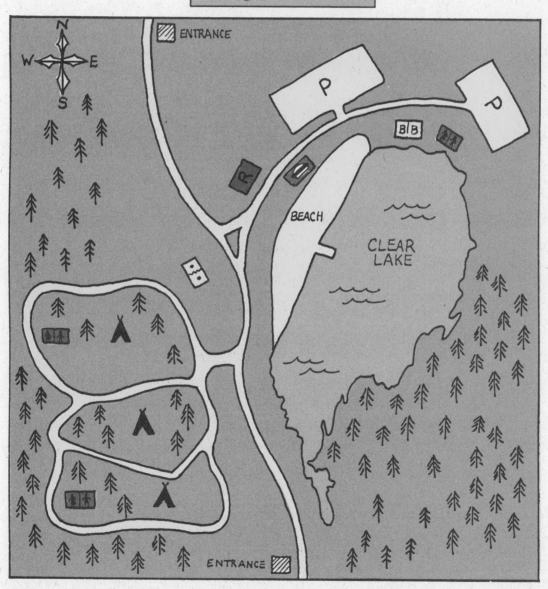

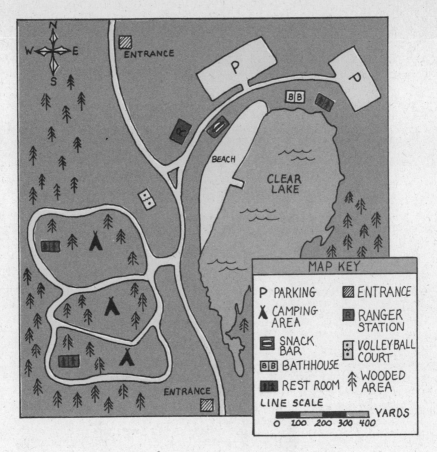

Use the map to answer the following questions.

1. BB is the symbol for the _____.

2. ⚡ is the symbol for the _____.

3. The symbol for the volleyball court looks like _____.

4. The symbol for the snack bar looks like _____.

5. About how far is it from the ranger station to the bathhouse?

_____

6. About how far is it from the north entrance to the south

entrance? _____

7. The north entrance is at the (top or bottom) _____ of the map.

8. How many rest rooms are shown on the map? _____

YOUR TURN

The state wants to build a park at Sunfish Pond. They need someone to design it. They want the park to include:

— a beach
— a camping area
— a snack bar
— a bathhouse
— several rest rooms
— a boathouse

You are hired to do the job. They give you a map of Sunfish Pond. Put everything that is needed on your map. Be sure to include a key.

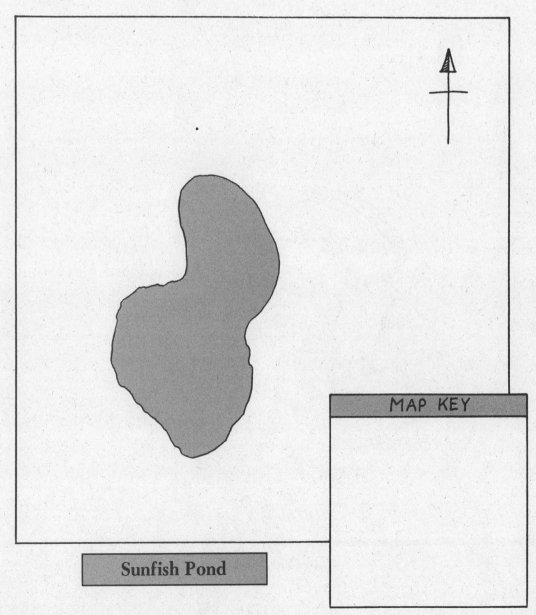

Sunfish Pond

MAP KEY

Chapter 11: AREA CODE MAPS

WORDS TO KNOW

> **area code**

To make long-distance phone calls, you need to know about area codes. An <u>area code</u> is a three-digit number. It goes before the telephone number.

(305) 123-4567
area code

Our country is divided into areas. Each area has an area code.

WHEN TO USE THE AREA CODE

You do not have to dial the area code every time you use the phone. Use the area code only when you are calling a place that has a **different** area code.

For example, Joe's area code is 305. His friend Frank lives in the next town. Frank's area code is also 305. When Joe calls Frank he just dials the phone number. He does not dial the area code. This is because the area codes are the same.

Joe's uncle lives in another state. His area code is 718. It is different from Joe's. When Joe calls his uncle he must dial 718 before he dials the phone number.

WHAT IF I DON'T KNOW THE AREA CODE?

There are two ways to find an area code. One way is to call information (1-555-1212). Tell the operator where you want to call. Give the operator both the city and state. The operator will tell you the area code for that city. This way sometimes costs you money. It will be charged to your telephone bill.

The second way is free. Use the area code map in the front of your telephone book. Generally, there are two maps. One is a map of the state in which you live. There is also a map of the United States.

Below is the area code map of Ohio.

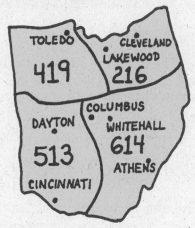

1. Find Toledo on the map. The area code for Toledo is

   _____ .

2. Find Dayton on the map. The area code for Dayton is

   _____ .

Area code map of Ohio

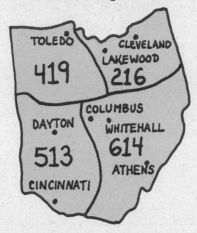

1. Anita lives in Cleveland. The area code for Cleveland is

   _____. She wants to call her friend in Lakewood.

2. The area code for Lakewood is _____. The area
   codes for Cleveland and Lakewood are the same.

3. Does Anita have to dial the area code when she calls her

   friend? _____

4. Michael lives in Columbus. The area code for Columbus is

   _____. He wants to make a call to Cincinnati.

5. The area code for Cincinnati is _____. The two area
   codes are different.

6. Does Michael have to use the area code when he calls

   Cincinnati? _____

7. Ellen's area code is 614. List three cities she could call

   without dialing the area code: _____,

   _____, _____.

8. List three cities she could call where she must dial the area

   code: _____, _____,

   _____.

Chapter 12: MORE FLOOR PLANS

In Chapter 1 you learned to draw floor plans. All the buildings in Chapter 1 had just one floor. Many buildings have more than one floor. Some buildings have many floors. The Sears Tower in Chicago has 110 floors. It is the largest building in the world.

Below is the floor plan for a two-floor building. It is really two floor plans. There is a floor plan for each floor.

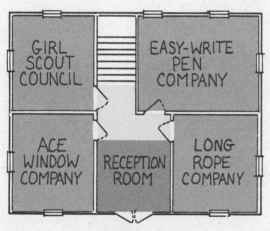

First Floor

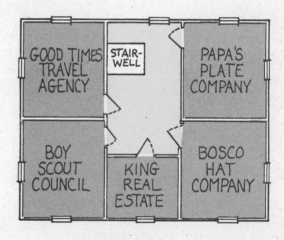

Second Floor

Look at the drawings. Find the first floor. Find the second floor. In your mind, picture the second floor stacked on top of the first floor. Then complete the following statements.

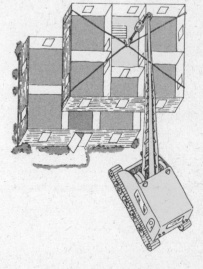

1. Good Times Travel Agency is directly **above** the _____

_____.

2. Long Rope Company is directly **below** the _____

_____.

Below is the floor plan for a two-floor house. Compare the two floors. The first floor is larger than the second floor.

Second Floor

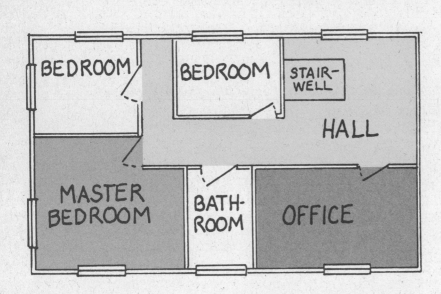

First Floor

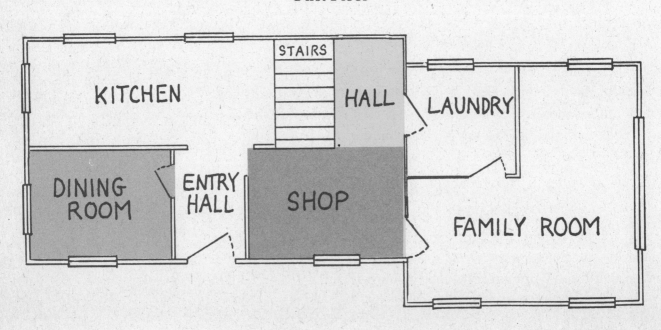

Look at the picture of the house. See how the second floor sits on the first. Now look at the floor plans. Picture how the second floor will fit on the first.

1. The master bedroom is directly **above** the _____

_____ .

2. The shop is directly **below** the _____

_____ .

Chapter 13: MAPS OF HISTORIC PLACES

George Washington's home is called Mount Vernon. Today it is a historic site. Thousands of people visit Mount Vernon every year.

When you visit Mount Vernon, you will receive a map like the one below. The map will help to guide you through the grounds. It will tell you about each building.

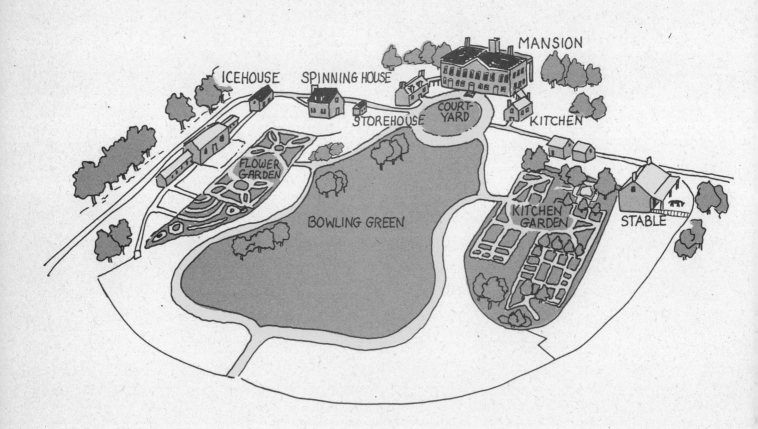

Use the map to answer the following questions.

1. The largest building is the _____.

2. The spinning house is between the _____

   and the _____.

3. The map shows two gardens. Which garden is closest to the

   stable? _____

4. Which is larger, the courtyard or the bowling green? _____

   _____

Today the amusement park opens. In the park there is a large parking lot. Joe and Rosa park near a sign that reads 5A.

The sign shows a map of the amusement park and a map of the parking lot. These maps will help Joe and Rosa to find their way around the park. They will help them to remember where they parked the car.

Look at the map. Find the parking lot. The car was parked in section 5A. Find section 5A on the map. Write "You Are Here" on section 5A.

Joe and Rosa want to go to the craft fair. Their friends Frank and Maria want to see the concert at the bandstand. Joe said, "Okay, but let's meet at the snack bar at 12:00 for lunch." Look closely at the map.

1. What is wrong with these directions?

    _____

    _____

    _____

    _____

Choose the best answer.

2. Which is closer to the picnic area? _____
    a. the water slide
    b. the bandstand
    c. the midway

3. The fun rides are between _____.
    a. the bandstand and the water slide
    b. the general store and the midway
    c. the bandstand and the craft fair

4. At the end of the day Joe and Rosa must return to the car. The car is in section 5A. From the entrance they should

    _____.

    a. turn left
    b. go straight
    c. turn right

Chapter 15: BUS MAPS

WORDS TO KNOW

schedule   route   timetable

People ride buses every day. Buses take people to and from work. They take people shopping and home again.

But how do people know where to catch the bus? How do they know what time the bus will arrive?

THE BUS SCHEDULE

A bus schedule will tell you where to catch the bus. It will tell you what time the bus will arrive.

Bus schedules have two parts. The first part is the map. The map shows where the bus will go. It shows the bus route.

Bus schedules also have timetables. Timetables help people to know what time the bus will arrive.

THE BUS MAP

A bus map shows the route the bus will take. Below is a map for Bus 24.

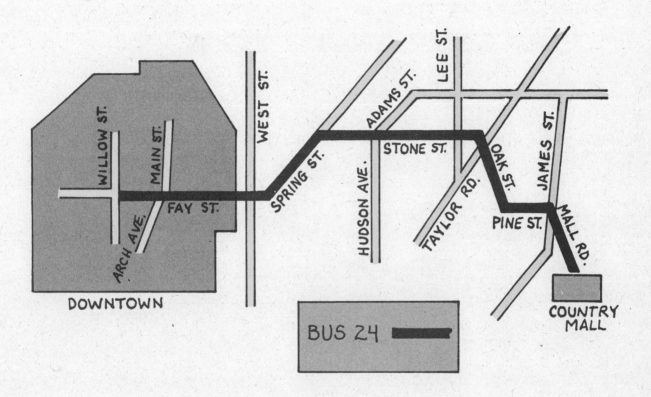

Look carefully at the map. Find the area marked downtown. Every morning Bus 24 leaves downtown. It travels the route shown on the map. Start downtown. With your pencil, trace the route the bus takes.

1. The last stop on the bus route is _____.

After the last stop the bus turns around. It goes back downtown. It travels the same route.

THE BUS TIMETABLE

The timetable tells what time the bus leaves its starting point. It tells what time it arrives at its final stop. The timetable for Bus 24 is explained below.

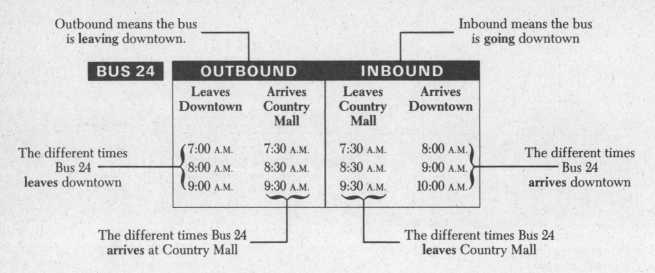

Outbound means the bus is **leaving** downtown.

Inbound means the bus is **going** downtown

The different times Bus 24 **leaves** downtown

The different times Bus 24 **arrives** downtown

The different times Bus 24 **arrives** at Country Mall

The different times Bus 24 **leaves** Country Mall

BUS 24	OUTBOUND		INBOUND	
	Leaves Downtown	Arrives Country Mall	Leaves Country Mall	Arrives Downtown
	7:00 A.M.	7:30 A.M.	7:30 A.M.	8:00 A.M.
	8:00 A.M.	8:30 A.M.	8:30 A.M.	9:00 A.M.
	9:00 A.M.	9:30 A.M.	9:30 A.M.	10:00 A.M.

Use the timetable to answer the questions below.

1. What time does the first bus **leave downtown**? _____

2. What time does that same bus **arrive at Country Mall**? _____

3. What time does the last bus **leave Country Mall**? _____

4. What time does that same bus **arrive downtown**? _____

Use the bus schedule below to answer questions 5 and 6.

OUTBOUND		INBOUND	
Leaves Downtown	Arrives Shay School	Leaves Shay School	Arrives Downtown
7:15 A.M.	8:00 A.M.	8:00 A.M.	8:45 A.M.
8:45 A.M.	9:30 A.M.	9:30 A.M.	10:15 A.M.
10:15 A.M.	11:00 A.M.	11:00 A.M.	11:45 A.M.

5. Frank lives on Front Street. Find Frank's house. The closest bus stop to

   Frank's house is at the intersection of _____

   and _____ .

6. Maria lives downtown. Every day she catches the 7:15 bus. What time does

   she arrive at Shay School? _____

Chapter 16: MAPS THAT HELP BUILD THINGS

WORDS TO KNOW

instructions	diagram

At the hardware store, Rosa saw a sign that said, "Sale on all birdhouses."

"A birdhouse would look nice in my yard," she thought. "I could hang it from the old maple tree."

She picked up one of the birdhouses and bought it. When she got home she opened the box. To her surprise, all she saw was eight pieces of wood and some nails.

"I have to put this together," she thought. "I've never built a birdhouse before. I don't know where to start."

Then she saw a piece of paper in the box. She looked at it. On the top, it said, "Instructions."

Rosa smiled. "Now I can build it," she thought. "I have the instructions."

INSTRUCTIONS ARE MAPS, TOO

<u>Instructions</u> are maps that help build things. Following instructions is like reading a map. Instructions tell you where to go and how to get there.

Below are the instructions to Rosa's birdhouse.

Instructions For Building Your Birdhouse

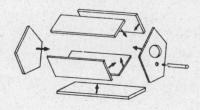

Tools you will need:
HAMMER   GLUE

Step 1: Nail both sides to front, as shown.

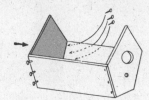

Step 2: Nail both sides to back, as shown.

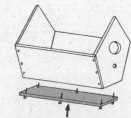

Step 3: Nail on bottom, as shown.

Step 4: Nail on both top pieces, as shown.

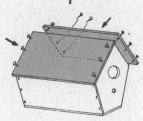

Step 5: Put a small amount of glue to the tip of the perch. Insert the perch into the small hole on the front piece.

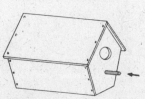

Your assembled birdhouse is now ready for use.

These instructions have two parts. The first part shows all the parts of the birdhouse. A picture called a <u>diagram</u> shows how the parts of the birdhouse fit together. The instructions also give a list of the tools Rosa will need to build the birdhouse.

The second part shows the order that the birdhouse should be put together. It gives step-by-step instructions.

Follow the instructions and diagram to answer the questions below.

1. The tools Rosa needs to build this birdhouse are

_____ and _____ .

2. When Rosa puts together the birdhouse, the first thing that

she needs to do is _____

_____ .

3. Rosa just nailed on the bottom piece of the birdhouse. What

is the next step? _____

_____

4. Why did Rosa use glue? _____

_____

Chapter 17: DIAGRAM OF AN AIRPLANE

WORDS TO KNOW

diagram

Maps can help guide you through almost anything. Below is a map of the inside of an airplane. It is also a <u>diagram</u>. The diagram shows the parts of the airplane and where things are.

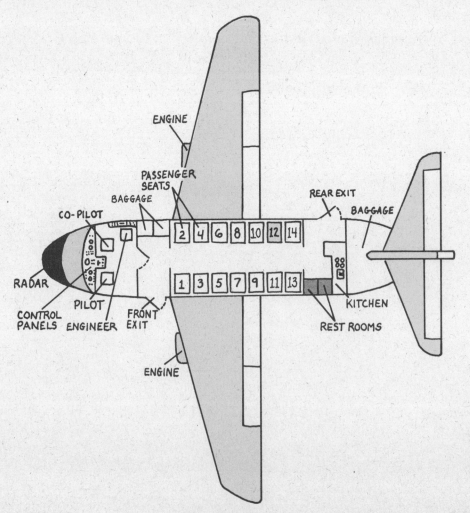

1. List five things you learned about this airplane from the diagram.

   a. _____

   _____ .

   b. _____

   _____ .

   c. _____

   _____ .

   d. _____

   _____ .

   e. _____

   _____ .

Imagine yourself on this airplane. Find seat number 12. Seat number 12 is your seat.

2. To get to the nearest exit, you would go to the (front, rear)

   _____ of the airplane.

3. To get to the rest rooms you would go to the (front, rear)

   _____ of the airplane.

4. How many exits does this airplane have? _____

5. How many passengers could this airplane hold without being

   overcrowded? (count the passenger seats) _____

GLOSSARY

area code . . . . . (**AIR** ē a cōd) Chapter 11: A three-digit number that goes before a phone number. The area code and the phone number must be dialed when you call long-distance.

compass . . . . . . (**KUM** pass) Chapter 6: A pointed figure drawn on a map to show direction. North is usually up on a map compass.

diagram . . . . . . (**DIE** a gram) Chapters 16, 17: A drawing that shows the parts of something. Often it shows how the parts are put together. Also a picture to show where things are.

directory . . . . . (di **REK** tor ē) Chapter 8: A list of names. In a mall map, the directory gives the name of the store and where to find that store on the map. A directory is always in alphabetical order.

expressway . . . (ek **SPRESS** wā) Chapter 4: A road designed for very fast travel.

floor plan . . . . . (**FLŌR** plan) Chapter 1: A map of a room or a building. The floor plan of a room outlines where the windows and the doors are. It also shows the outline of the furniture.

forecast . . . . (**FŌR** kast) Chapter 9: A prediction of the weather. A forecast tells what weather we think will come.

grid . . . . (grid) Chapter 5: A crisscross of lines that breaks a map into small squares.

index . . . . (**IN** deks) Chapter 5: A list of places shown on a map. The index gives the name of the place and the name of the grid square. The grid square tells you where that place is on the map. An index is always in alphabetical order.

instructions . . . (in **STRUK** shunz) Chapter 16: A guide that tells you how to do something. Instructions can tell you how to put something together.

intersection . . . (**IN** ter **SEK** shun) Chapter 3: A crossing, especially where two or more streets cross each other.

key . . . . (kē) Chapter 4: Part of a map that explains the symbols used on the map.

line scale . . . . . (**LĪN** skāl) Chapter 7: A type of scale used on a map. A line that is broken into a series of sections. Each section is equal to a certain distance on the map.

map . . . . (map) Introduction: A drawing, usually on a piece of paper, of a country, region, or a city. It is used to help us find places.

rain . . . . (rān) Chapter 9: Rain occurs in a steady pattern. Rain usually lasts a long time.

road map . . . . . (**RŌD** map) Chapter 4: A drawing showing a certain area and its roads. These roads are usually major routes between cities or regions.

route . . . . (root) Chapter 15: A road or course taken to get from one place to another.

scale . . . . (skāl) Chapter 7: A way of measuring distance on a map. The distance on a scale is compared to the distance on a map. The scale shows the real distance between two points.

schedule . . . . . . (**SKEJ** yool) Chapter 15: A schedule for a bus tells you where to catch the bus and what time the bus will arrive. It contains a map and a timetable.

showers . . . . . . (**SHOW** erz) Chapter 9: Showers are short rain falls. A shower doesn't usually last for a long time.

street map . . . . (**STRĒT** map) Chapter 3: A map that shows all the streets in a neighborhood or city.

symbol . . . . (**SIM** bul) Chapter 4: Something chosen to stand for something else. On a map, a symbol for an oil well stands for a real oil well.

timetable . . . . . (**TĪM** tā bl) Chapter 15: A schedule showing when something is going to happen. A timetable shows when buses, trains, or planes are going to leave and arrive.

top view . . . . . . (**TOP** vyoo) Chapter 1: On a map, things are shown as if they were drawn looking down from high above. This is called the top view.

ANSWER KEY

Chapter 1

p. 12 1. 2
        2. 1
        3. 2

Chapter 2

p. 15 1. furniture
        2. a. 4
            b. 6
            c. /\
            d. ▭

p. 16 1. 11
        2. 7
        3. stairs

Chapter 3

p. 21 1. Cory's Store
        2. Baker
        3. Lincoln Park

p. 22 1. Oak Drive
        2. Lincoln Park
        3. Joe's house
        4. Orange Street

p. 23 1. Rockville School

p. 24 1. Enjoy Park, Jake's Bait Shop
        2. Big B Market
        3. Grant Street, Vermont Avenue
        4. Washington Street, Central Avenue

Chapter 4

p. 25 1. tree
        2. house
        3. railroad tracks
        4. river

p. 26 1. baseball field
        2. house
        3. 🏫
        4. Ⓟ
        5. 2
        6. College Street, Main Street

p. 27 1. •
        2. ◯
        3. Canton, Oceanview, Rock Falls, Old Town
        4. Orange City, Mapleton
        5. 4

p. 28 1. 61
        2. 13, 61
        3. Answers will vary

p. 29 1. Texas

Chapter 5

p. 33 1. 2A
        2. 4B
        3. 2C
        4. Ben's house
        5. Pine Grove

Chapter 6

p. 40 1. b., go straight through the intersection

Chapter 7

p. 41 1. model A

p. 43 1. 200 miles
         2. 300 miles
         3. 500 miles
         4. 50 miles

p. 44 1. 1 inch = 100 feet
         2. ½ inch = 20 miles
         3. 1 inch = 1000 miles

p. 45 1. a. 1 inch = 10 miles
            b. 2
            c. 20 miles
            d. 20 miles
            e. 10 miles
            f. 30 miles

p. 48 1. 30 miles
         2. 40 miles
         3. 20 miles
         4. 10 miles

Chapter 8

p. 51 1. a., next to store number 1
         2. a. 5
            b. 13
            c. 11
            d. 2

Chapter 9

p. 52 1. c., what kind of weather is coming

p. 53 1. b., Sunday's weather
         2. partly sunny
         3. snow
         4. showers
         5. ☀
         6. ///
         7. rain
         8. snow
         9. sunny
       10. partly sunny
       11. showers

p. 54 1. a., rain steadily
         2. b., rain on and off

Chapter 10

p. 56 1. bathhouse
         2. wooded area
         3. ⠿
         4. ▤
         5. 300 yards
         6. 1100 yards
         7. top
         8. three

Chapter 11

p. 59 1. 419
         2. 513

p. 60 1. 216
         2. 216
         3. No
         4. 614
         5. 513
         6. Yes
         7. Athens, Columbus, Whitehall
         8. Dayton, Toledo, Cleveland, Cincinnati, Lakewood

Chapter 12

p. 61   1.   Girl Scout Council
        2.   Bosco Hat Company

p. 63   1.   dining room
        2.   office

Chapter 13

p. 65   1.   mansion
        2.   icehouse, storehouse
        3.   the kitchen garden
        4.   the bowling green

Chapter 14

p. 67   1.   There are two snack bars; Joe told his friends to meet him at the snack bar, but he did not say which one.
        2.   c., the midway
        3.   c., the bandstand and the craft fair
        4.   c., turn right

Chapter 15

p. 69   1.   Country Mall

p. 70   1.   7:00 A.M.
        2.   7:30 A.M.
        3.   9:30 A.M.
        4.   10:00 A.M.
        5.   Main Street, Adams Street
        6.   8:00 A.M.

Chapter 16

p. 73   1.   hammer, glue
        2.   nail both sides to front
        3.   nail on both top pieces
        4.   to glue the perch to the birdhouse

Chapter 17

p. 75   1.   Answers will vary.
        2.   rear
        3.   rear
        4.   2
        5.   14